What is a map?

A map is simply a drawing or picture of a landscape or location. Maps usually show the landscape as it would be seen from above, looking directly down.

As well as showing the landscape of an area, maps will often show other features such as roads, rivers, buildings, trees and lakes.

A map can allow you to accurately plan a journey, giving a good idea of landmarks and features you will pass along the route, as well as how far you will be travelling.

Understanding your map needs

There are many different types of maps. The type of map you would choose depends on why you need it. If you were trying to find a certain street or building in your home town you would need a map that showed you all the smaller streets, maybe even footpaths in and around town.

If you were trekking across a mountain range you might need a map that shows a bigger area of land and tells you the heights and steepness of the mountains.

If you were a pilot flying from London to Edinburgh you might need a map that has the whole of the country on a single page, with only the locations of towns and cities on it. Whichever type you choose, there are a few basic features usually found on any map, which will be explained in this leaflet.

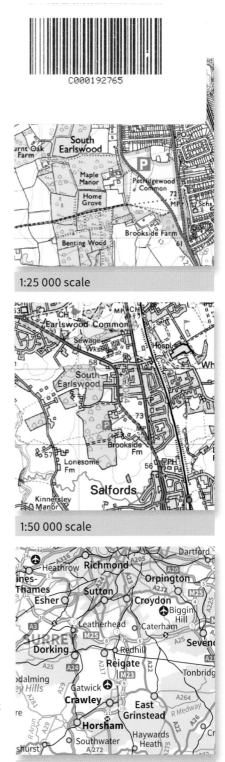

1:25 000 scale

1:50 000 scale

1:1 000 000 scale

Map symbols explained

Rather than containing descriptions, maps have symbols to show where certain things are. Symbols are used so maps don't have to be covered in writing, as this would make them very confusing.

Ordnance Survey uses different shapes, colours and symbols to show all the roads, buildings, rivers and other features of a landscape. Symbols are designed to be simple, often looking like the features they represent. This means things can be quickly and easily recognised as you look at a map.

The symbols here are actually used on Ordnance Survey maps. Write down what you think they represent:

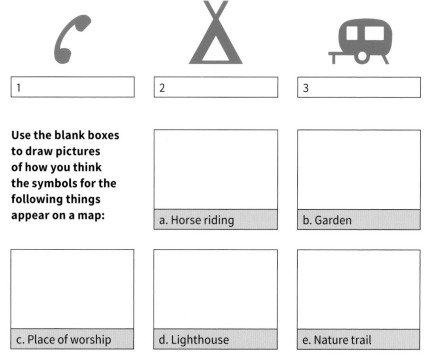

1

2

3

Use the blank boxes to draw pictures of how you think the symbols for the following things appear on a map:

a. Horse riding

b. Garden

c. Place of worship

d. Lighthouse

e. Nature trail

Here's where you find out how you did...

The answers to the first three questions are a telephone call box, a campsite and a caravan site.

To find out how close your drawings are to actual Ordnance Survey symbols you can look at the key on an Ordnance Survey map.

Maps will usually have a key or a legend. This is a section that will explain what each and every symbol on the map represents. If you find something on the map you don't understand or recognise, the key or legend will help you to identify what it is.

Map scale: What it means

To create an accurate picture of a landscape on paper everything has to be made much, much smaller. This is done by 'scaling down' the actual size of the land.

The map below shows Great Britain. The size of the island has been 'scaled down' so it will fit on this sheet of paper. The map is too small to contain a lot of detail and doesn't have many names on it, as there isn't much room.

Scale: 1:6 000 000

Understanding your map 1. The basics

There are some basic features that most maps will include:

- **Roads** tend to be marked in different colours depending on the type of road depicted. Roads on a map range from thick blue lines, showing motorways, to dashed lines, indicating an unfenced minor road.
- **Footpaths** are marked on Ordnance Survey maps in various colours. On a 1:25 000 scale OS Explorer Map the public rights of way are marked in green and on a 1:50 000 scale OS Landranger Map they are marked in magenta. There are various types of public rights of way and public access, so please check the map key for full information. It is important to be aware that footpaths that are shown in black are not necessarily public rights of way.
- **Woods** are shown in green with a coniferous or non-coniferous tree shape printed over the top.
- **Buildings** are marked by small black squares. However, some particular buildings have their own special symbols, such as churches and windmills. Any of these buildings can be useful landmarks, helping you to check your position on the map.
- **Rivers and streams** are shown as blue lines. The width of the line is representative of the watercourse width (if the width of a river is more than 8 metres it is shown as two blue lines with a light blue area between). Rivers and streams can be extremely useful in determining your position on a map.
- **Scale** tells you how much the land has been scaled down to fit on the paper. If the scale of a map is 1:50 000 then everything on the map will be 50 000 times smaller than it is in reality.
- **Your Ordnance Survey map** will also contain other features and information that will be explained, along with the features above, in the key of the map.

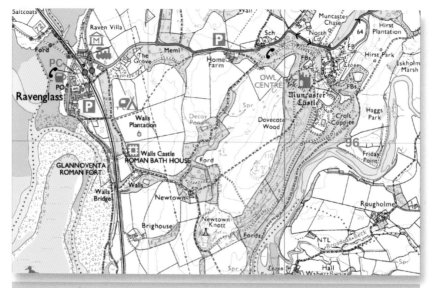

1:25 000 scale

Understanding your map 2. Grid lines explained

Ordnance Survey maps are covered in a series of faint blue lines that make up a grid. The lines have numbers accompanying them that allow you to accurately pinpoint your location on a map. Once you have located where you are, the grid system makes it simple to give others (such as mountain rescue) an accurate description of your location. This description, which will be a series of numbers, is known as a grid reference.

Grid references

Before you begin to look at grid references it is important to be aware that all the numbers going across the face of the map, for example, left to right, are called eastings (this is because they are heading eastward), and similarly, all the numbers going up the face of the map from bottom to top are called northings (again because they are heading in a northward direction).

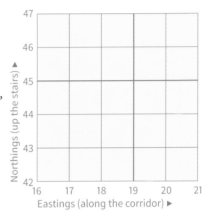

There are two main types of grid reference:

- **4-figure** – for example, **1945**, this indicates a single kilometre square on an Ordnance Survey map.
- **6-figure** – for example, **192454**, shows a point within a square.

4-figure map references

When giving a 4-figure grid reference you should always give the eastings number first and the northings number second, very much like when giving the reading of a graph in school – you must go along the corridor/hallway (horizontal) and then up the stairs (vertical).

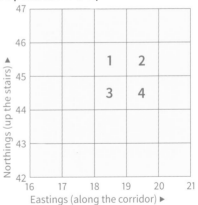

For example, the number **2** in the diagram opposite is **19** across and **45** up and therefore the 4-figure grid reference is **1945**.

The numbered squares on the diagram above would have the following 4-figure grid references:

1 = **18 45** 2 = **19 45**
3 = **18 44** 4 = **19 44**

6-figure map references

Having worked out the basic 4-figure grid reference, for example, square 3 below, imagine this square is further divided up into tenths. Using the example opposite, the grey box is in the square **1844**. More accurately it is 7 tenths across and 8 tenths up within the grid square **1844** and therefore has the 6-figure map reference **187448**.

The shapes on the diagram would have the following 6-figure grid references:

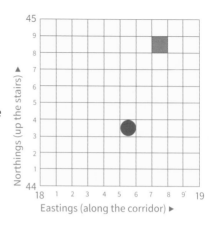

 = 187448   = 185443

National Grid lines

As well as numbered grid lines, Ordnance Survey maps have codes made of two letters. These two letter codes can be found printed in faint blue capitals on Ordnance Survey maps. The whole of Great Britain is divided into squares of 100 km and each square is given two letters. There will be a diagram within your map's key showing you which areas of your map fall into different squares of the National Grid.

When you quote your six-digit grid reference you should put the two letters of the area you are in before the numbers. This means that there is no doubt or confusion about your location. For example, you may be at grid reference **509 582** in south-west Scotland. The complete grid reference you should quote would be **NX 509 582** (without the letters the numeric reference would be repeated in every 100 km square).

			HO	HP		
			HT	HU		
	HW	HX	HY	HZ		
NA	NB	NC	ND	NE		
NF	NG	NH	NJ	NK		
NL	NM	NN	NO	NP		
	NR	NS	NT	NU		
	NW	NX	NY	NZ	OV	
		SC	SD	SE	TA	
		SH	SJ	SK	TE	TG
	SM	SN	SO	SP	TL	TM
	SR	SS	ST	SU	TQ	TR
SV	SW	SX	SY	SZ	TV	

Understanding your map 3. Reading contours and relief

Understanding the shape of the land by looking at a map is a very useful skill and can be essential if you're going to be walking in mountainous terrain. The height and shape of the land is shown on a map using 'contour lines'. These lines appear as thin orange or brown lines with numbers on them. The number tells you the height above sea level of that line.

A contour line is drawn between points of the same height, so any single contour line will be at the same height all the way along its length. The height difference between separate contour lines is normally 5 metres, but it will be 10 metres in very hilly or mountainous areas. The map key will tell you the contour interval used.

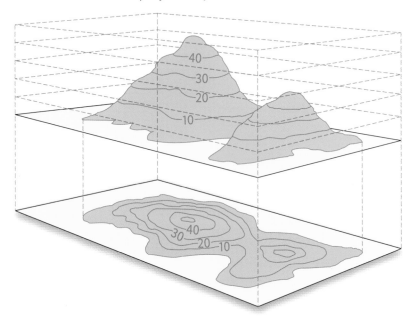

The picture shown illustrates how a landscape can be converted into contour lines on a map. An easy way to understand and visualise contour lines is to think of them as high tide lines that would be left by the sea. As the water level drops it would leave a line every 10 metres on the landscape. These marks would be contour lines.

Being able to visualise the shape of the landscape by looking at the contour lines of a map is a very useful skill that can be developed with practice. It will allow you to choose the best route for your journey. When reading contour lines on a map it's helpful to remember the numbering on them reads uphill. It might be useful to imagine that to read contour line numbers you have to be stood at the bottom of the hill looking up it, otherwise the numbers would be upside down.

Other useful things to look out for when reading contour lines are rivers, which usually flow into valleys, or areas with very few contour lines, which will be flat.

The picture below shows how contour lines can be used on maps to describe different landscapes. Even though all the lines look similar at first, they are describing very different landscape features. The closer together the contour lines, the steeper the slope of the hill. If a hill is very steep the contour lines might even merge into each other.

A spur is a 'V'-shaped hill that juts out. A simple way to tell a valley from a spur when looking at contour lines is to remember that if the 'V' points uphill it's a valley, if it points downhill it's a spur.

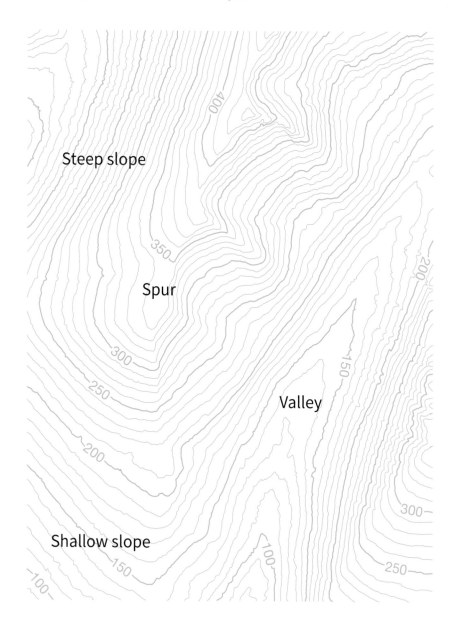

Now you have the skills and knowledge to read and understand a map, the next step is to learn how to orientate your map to the land so that you can use it to navigate. One of the best ways to orientate your map is with a compass. The picture below shows a compass, explaining its various features.

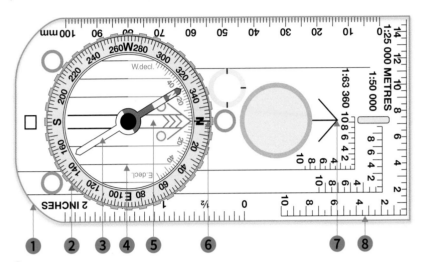

1 The base plate
The mounting of the compass, with a ruler for measuring scale.

2 The compass housing
Contains the magnetic **needle** and has the points of the compass printed on a circular, rotating bezel.

3 The compass needle
Floats on liquid so it can rotate freely, the red end should always point to magnetic north.

4 Orienting lines
Fixed within the compass housing and designed to be aligned with the eastings on a map. On some compasses half the lines are coloured red to indicate north.

5 Orienting arrow
Fixed within the compass housing, aligned to north on the housing.

6 The index line
Fixed within the outer edge of the compass housing as an extension of the direction of travel arrow. It marks the bearing you set by rotating the compass housing.

7 The direction of travel arrow
Shows the direction that you want to travel along or the bearing you are taking. It is fixed parallel to the sides of the base plate.

8 Compass scale
Displayed along the edge of the base plate so you can measure distances on maps.

Understanding your map

Decide on the route of your walk and identify your starting point on the map. Place your compass on the map. Make sure the 'direction of travel arrow' is pointing in the direction of your route across the map. The easiest way to line the arrow is to place the side of the base plate so it crosses your starting point and the next destination of your journey.

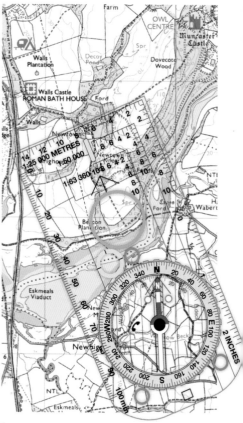

Carefully holding the compass base plate still, you will need to turn the compass housing so the orientating lines match up with the eastings (the vertical, north–south lines) on your map. Holding the map flat and the compass still, you need to rotate your body so that the compass needle settles in line (opposite) with the index line. To fully orientate your map you will need to make some adjustments for magnetic variation.

Adjustments for magnetic variation

One thing to remember is that your compass does not point to the true north – except by coincidence in some areas. The compass needle is attracted by magnetic force, which varies in different parts of the world and is constantly changing. The magnetic variation throughout Great Britain currently ranges from 2º to 6º. The amount of variation changes every year, so check your Ordnance Survey map to work out the most current value.

You can properly orientate the map by carefully turning the compass housing 4º clockwise (for example, depending on where you are in Great Britain) and then turning your body again to realign the magnetic needle with the index line. Your map is now oriented to the north.

A word of caution

Compass readings are also affected by the presence of iron and steel objects, so be sure to look out for – and stay away from – pocket knives, belt buckles, railroad tracks and so forth when using your compass.

Using land features

As an alternative to using a compass to orientate your map, you can use your eyesight. This method will only work if you are in an area with visible prominent features or landmarks.

First, locate yourself next to a feature or landmark and place your finger on the map at the point where you are standing. Then begin to rotate the map so that other features and landmarks on the map begin to line up with the actual ones you can see. The map is now orientated with the land, although not as accurately as it would be using a compass.

And finally...

OK, so now you can read a map. But before you put on your boots and pack your rucksack, take the time to read through the following handy tips and safety points to ensure you get the most from your adventures.

1. Pre-plan your route

Before you set out, take the time to plot your route and mark it on your map. This will ensure your eyes are immediately drawn to the correct part of the map. If it's your first expedition with a map and compass, start with a short route in an area you're familiar with.

2. Make sure you have the right equipment

- A map of the area you are exploring, and map case will help to protect your map from bad weather.
- A compass with a base plate and a circular, rotating housing.
- A pencil, in case you decide to plan and orientate a new route.
- A watch, to make sure that you can keep track of time.
- And enough food and water to see you through your journey.
- Check the weather forecast in advance so you have appropriate clothing with you.

3. Tell someone where you're going

Always remember to tell either a family member or a friend where you're going and when you expect to be back.

4. Abide by the Countryside Code

- Be safe – plan ahead and follow any signs.
- Leave gates and property as you find them.
- Protect plants and animals, and take your litter home.
- Keep your dog under close control.
- Consider other people.

Advanced techniques

This part of the booklet will introduce you to some advanced map-reading techniques that can be useful when navigating. These techniques are largely used when you are off the beaten track in mountainous or difficult terrain, where excellent navigation skills are essential. Before reading this part you should have a good understanding of how to use a compass and map to navigate.

Techniques to pinpoint your location

There are several techniques to help pinpoint your location on a map. Pinpointing your location is useful to make sure you're moving in the right direction or can help you to relocate if you are lost. These techniques can be used very effectively once you've learned to interpret the features of a map. Some methods will rely on your eyesight while others use your compass.

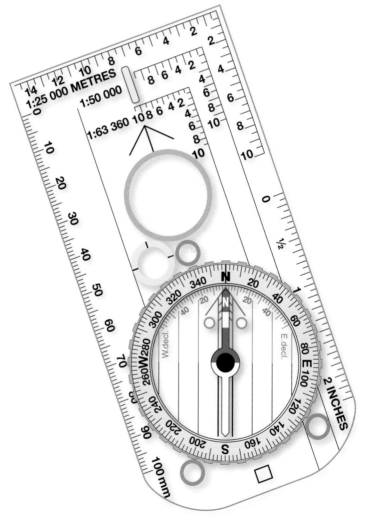

Pinpointing your location 1. Transit lines

When you know two or more features on a map will line up with one another along your journey you can form a transit line. As you walk along a track (which appears on the map) there will only be a single point where two features appear in a direct line with each other.

Draw a line on the map that crosses through both features and continues across the track you're walking on. When you see the two features on the landscape line up as you walk along the track, you'll be at the point where the line on your map crosses the track (as shown here).

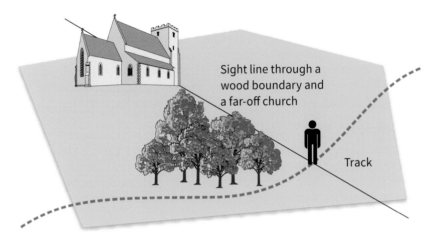

Sight line through a wood boundary and a far-off church

Track

It's also possible to create transit lines using linear features such as walls, fences or straight streams, even if the features won't line up as they did above. By drawing lines on a map, extending the existing lines of linear features, you can create several transit lines that will help you pinpoint your location (as shown below).

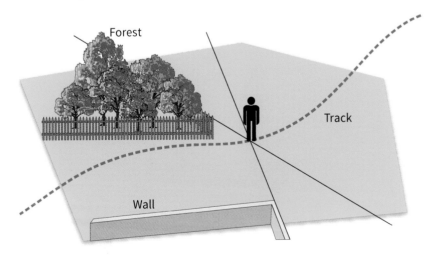

Forest

Track

Wall

Pinpointing your location 2. Back bearings

An alternative to using transit lines, and relying on sight, is to use a compass to locate your position.

If you are on a known track with an identifiable feature in sight (which also appears on your map) you can take a bearing in the direction of the feature and use it to calculate your location. Looking at your compass, detect the direction the feature is from your current location. With the direction of travel arrow pointing at the feature, turn the compass housing so the orienting line sits under the red half of the compass needle.

This bearing is a magnetic bearing rather than a grid bearing, which your map uses. You need to deduct magnetic variation from the compass reading to convert it. The magnetic variation is currently 2° to 6° throughout Great Britain (this amount changes annually, so check your Ordnance Survey map to work out the most current value). Revolve the compass housing 4° clockwise (for example) to deduct magnetic variation, and place the compass on your map.

Line the orienting lines up with the eastings (the grid lines running north–south) on your map. Now carefully slide the compass across the map so one of the edges of the base plate crosses the feature you spotted on the landscape on the map. If possible, draw a line along the base plate. Where the line crosses the track you are on is your approximate current location.

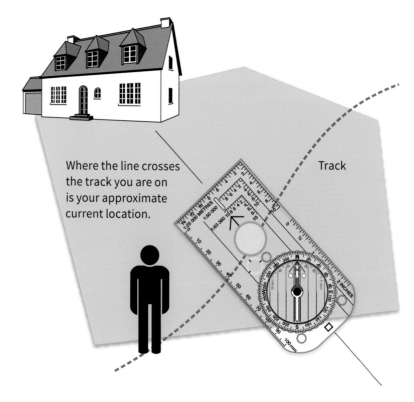

Where the line crosses the track you are on is your approximate current location.

Track

Pinpointing your location 3. Resection

A resection is similar to a back bearing but can be used if you are in the middle of open countryside or on an unknown track.

You need to begin by taking the bearings of three features in sight, which are also on your map (if there are no man-made features use natural features such as the crests of hills).

The three features should be spread out, ideally with 120° between each (for example, one in front of you, one if you look over your right shoulder and the other over your left shoulder). It is possible to use two features, but this will severely affect the accuracy of your pinpointing.

Repeat the steps you took to obtain a single back bearing for all three features you can see. You should now have three lines drawn on your map, creating a small triangle where they cross one another. Inside the triangle is your approximate current location.

Three back bearings cross
to create a triangle – this is
your approximate location

Pinpointing your location 4. Aspect of slope

If you are lost, slopes can often provide vital clues to help pinpoint your location. You will need to know which km square on the map's grid you are in. Stand facing directly down a slope, imagining you are at 90° to the contour lines of the slope. Using your compass, take a reading of the direction the hill is sloping in and make a note of the reading. This reading is known as the 'slope aspect'.

Looking at the km square on your map, try to find a slope that faces in the same direction as the reading you've just taken. This will help you to establish an approximate location. Taking back bearings will also help. To improve accuracy, walk to another nearby slope, take another reading and then look for this on your map. If you come across a distinguishing feature, such as a spur or valley, measure its slope aspect and look for it on the map. This will help you narrow down or even pinpoint your location. Measuring the aspect of slope is particularly useful if you are lost and find yourself in a bowl or on the end of a spur or ridge.

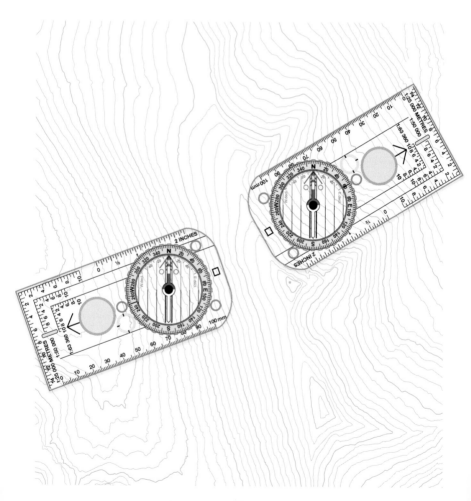

Feature interpretation

In remote and difficult terrain man-made features can often be rare. It's also possible a man-made feature, such as a log cabin, can be added or removed from the landscape. Since natural features don't change as quickly or easily as their man-made counterparts, being able to use them to navigate is essential.

Interpreting the shape of the land on a map using contour lines is an extremely useful navigational tool. Looking at the lines and creating a mental picture of the landscape will allow you to plan a journey effectively. Orange or brown contour lines on maps join points of equal height above sea level together, and are usually measured in 5- or 10-metre height intervals.

One of the easiest ways to convert contour lines into a mental picture is to imagine the lines as high tide marks left by the sea. As the water level drops it leaves a line every 5 or 10 metres on the landscape, forming the contour lines.

It's worth bearing in mind that smaller features may be missed by contour lines. If a feature is 9 metres high on the land it may not appear on a map with contour lines at 10 metre intervals. This can be surprising when you see the actual landscape and it contains features you haven't imagined since they don't appear on your map.

When interpreting contour lines you can use symbols and features around them to get a better understanding of how the landscape will appear in reality. In particular, you should look for the symbols for cliffs, outcrops, scree and streams, as they will give you a valuable insight into the formation of a landscape.

When calculating the distance of your journey on a map you need to remember the actual distance you are going to travel along the ground will be further than the map implies. The two dimensions of a map don't show you the actual distances of slopes you will be travelling up and down, adding to the overall distance you walk.

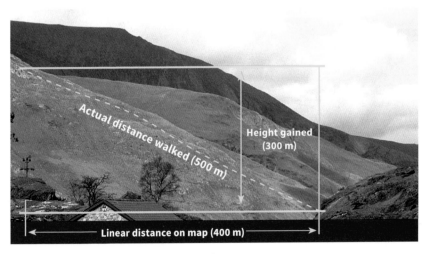

Contouring

When planning your route on a map it pays to remember that the straightest line between your starting point and destination may not be the easiest, quickest or safest. Examine the map of the area you are walking in very carefully before planning a route. If you are going to be walking in mountainous or rough terrain it is often a good idea to plan a route following contour lines. This is called 'contouring'.

Contouring can allow you to avoid walking over the top of large hills and mountains, potentially saving you time and energy. When planning the route you should consider the distance of the journey, the weather conditions, the amount of equipment being carried and the fitness levels of the walkers before deciding whether to tackle the slopes or to contour around them.

Many leisure walkers will avoid contouring in favour of climbing slopes for a great view or sense of achievement. In harsh conditions, where speed and efficiency are essential, contouring is often the best option.

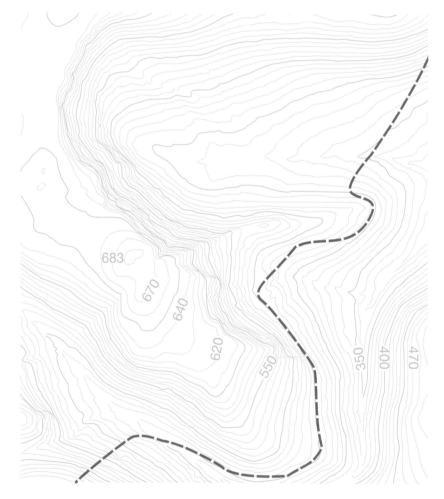

Measuring the distance travelled 1. On the ground

You now know the direction you need to be heading in, but it would be expecting too much from both your equipment and yourself to be able to reach your target spot on. So you must be able to tell when you have missed your target location and have gone too far. As much as possible you need to track your position on the ground while you are walking. This can done using features both on the map and on the ground.

The first step is to use your map to measure the distance to your next checkpoint. If you haven't got a ruler, use the millimetre scale on your compass. On a map with a scale of 1:25 000 each millimetre is worth 25 metres, or on a 1:50 000 scale map each is worth 50 metres, and so on.

You then need to measure your distance on the ground. There are two ways of doing this:

Pacing – To pace successfully you need to know in advance how many double paces you can take for every 100 metres. Double pacing is better than single as it reduces the level of counting. It is estimated that a person of average height will take 65 double paces every 100 metres, but it is vital you work it out to your own pace count. Please do this by walking normally. Remember slopes or poor conditions underfoot will require an adjustment and steep slopes will shorten your stride dramatically.

Timing – If you know, or can at least guess, how fast you are walking you can work out how long it is going to take you to walk from your starting point to your next target location. At 4 km/hr, which is an 'average' speed, it will take you 1.5 minutes to cover each 100 metres, so a leg of 700 metres should take you 10.5 minutes to walk. Again, as with pacing, this will be affected by slopes, poor underfoot conditions and other factors, so you will have to adjust your time accordingly.

Measuring the distance travelled 2. Naismith's rule

As previously mentioned, measuring the time you take to travel a certain distance is all well and good if you are travelling on a flat landscape. However, in reality this won't be the case. With this in mind, a Scottish climber called Naismith created a simple but effective formula that took into account the changes in height while calculating speed over the ground – 5 km/hr plus ½ hour for every 300 metres of ascent.

For convenience, this formula is often expressed in terms of extra time required to climb a given number of contour lines – for example, it takes an additional minute to climb one 10-metre contour line or an additional 5 minutes for each thick contour line. On a descending slope it is assumed that you will be walking faster on shallow slopes but possibly a lot slower on steep descents – it is therefore taken that this will even out over the course of a day's walk.

Can't find your next location? Walking on a bearing

As you walk on a bearing, errors will undoubtedly creep into the actual direction you are travelling and the distance you have measured. For example, when walking across a slope on a compass bearing you will tend to stray off slightly downhill. Also, your pacing may become inaccurate as a result of difficult terrain.

To help counteract this, choose closer checkpoints, preferably between 1 000 m and 500 m – but this will ultimately depend on the terrain you are crossing. Also, try lining up a distant object on your bearing and walk towards it with your eyes constantly on the object and not on your map and compass – this will help to prevent veering off course.

There are a couple of methods you can use when walking on a bearing to help guarantee you reach your chosen checkpoint.

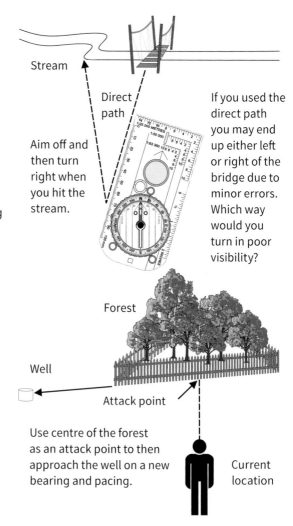

Aiming off – If your checkpoint is on a linear feature such as a stream or a track, by simply aiming off slightly to one side of the checkpoint, you can guarantee which direction you need to head to reach your checkpoint upon hitting the linear feature.

Stream

Direct path

Aim off and then turn right when you hit the stream.

If you used the direct path you may end up either left or right of the bridge due to minor errors. Which way would you turn in poor visibility?

Attack points – To locate difficult features simply find another definite, prominent feature nearby and make your way to the centre of it. Once there use pacing to find the original feature you are looking for – as shown in the diagram.

Forest

Well

Attack point

Use centre of the forest as an attack point to then approach the well on a new bearing and pacing.

Current location

Still can't find your next location?

If, after following one of the previous measuring methods, you arrive at an area but cannot see your next chosen checkpoint – often due to poor visibility – refer back to your map and look for any distinguishing features or clues. If you can't see what you are looking for, you will have to do a systematic search of the area to locate your next point. There are two types of search you can undertake:

Spiral search – This is a good method to use if you are alone and have limited visibility. From your current position, use your compass and walk north to the limit of your visibility. Stop and use your compass, turn 90° to the right and walk twice the limit of your visibility (you will have to pace accurately). Stop again and turn right through another 90° and walk three times the limit of your visibility. Keep repeating this process with longer and longer legs until you find your checkpoint or object.

All areas on search are visible at some point

Sweep search – A drawback of the sweep search is that it is difficult to carry out alone, but can be easily undertaken by a party of walkers. Using the sweep method is relatively simple. Space everyone out so that you are all still within visible contact and sweep backwards and forwards across the area to be searched until your checkpoint or object is located.

Note: To work out the limit of visibility distance, ask someone to pace away from you. Stop them when it becomes difficult to see them – this is your distance. If you are unable to do this, guess the distance, making sure you underestimate rather than overestimate it.

Navigating at night or in bad weather

Navigating in fair conditions should present no great problems to an advanced walker. Poor conditions don't require new techniques, just a more skilful and determined use of those you already possess. Nevertheless, it is important to draw attention to certain aspects that require special consideration that would prepare you for such conditions:

- Your route plan should note possible escape paths along your route, have a record of compass bearings, distances and estimated times.
- Check through your equipment before you set off to make sure everything is in working order.
- Make sure you have easy access to essential equipment when you pack your rucksack.
- Use a map case to protect your map from bad weather or use an OS Explorer Map – Active.

Remember, advanced planning can help ease stress if you find yourself in a difficult situation.

1. Planning a perfect day out
2. The durable all-weather leisure planning map
3. The essential map for outdoor activities
4. For people who love extremes
5. For touring and local route planning

Contact details

www.ordnancesurvey.co.uk
customerservices@ordnancesurvey.co.uk

General enquiries: +44 (0)8456 05 05 05
Dedicated Welsh Language HelpLine: 08456 05 05 04
Textphone (deaf and hard of hearing users only please): +44 (0)23 8005 6146

Customer Service Centre, Ordnance Survey,
Adanac Drive, SOUTHAMPTON, SO16 0AS.

ISBN: 978-0-319-08801-2

9 780319 088012